SIOP® Training for Teachers

Participant Workbook

ISBN 1-4029-3731-8
ISBN 978-1-4029-3731-6

3 4 5 6 7 8 9 10 11 16 15 14 13 12 11 10 09 08

Contents

DAY 1

Welcome/Program Overview

Session 1: Second Language Acquisition Theories

Session 2: Introduction to Sheltered Instruction and the SIOP® Model

Contents

DAY 1 (continued)

Session 3: Lesson Preparation

Session 4: Building Background

DAY 2

Welcome Back/Day 2 Overview

Session 5: Comprehensible Input

Contents

DAY 2 (continued)

Contents

DAY 3

Welcome Back/Day 3 Overview

Session 9: Lesson Delivery

Session 10: Review and Assessment

Session 11: Implementing the SIOP Model

Session 12: Lesson Planning

Appendix

Sessions

Day 1

Welcome/ Program Overview

Ice-Breaker: Group Hello

Please think of one major challenge facing English learners in your school.

Operating Principles

- Surface assumptions

- Ask clarifying questions

- Reserve judgment

- Actively listen to self and others

Word Wall

You will likely hear the following terms used as you learn about the SIOP Model:

EL	English (language) learner
SEI	Sheltered/Structured English Immersion Sheltered/Structured English Instruction
SIOP®	SIOP® Model SIOP® (Sheltered Instruction Observation Protocol)
SWBAT	Students Will Be Able To
L1	Abbreviation for primary or native language
L2	Abbreviation for target language, second language, or new language being learned by student

List other new terms you learn in the spaces below.

Day 1
Content and Language Objectives

Morning Objectives

Content:

- Identify eight specified factors that affect second language acquisition and one key point about each.
- Distinguish between conversational language and academic language in second language acquisition theories.
- Relate knowledge of the research that supports the SIOP Model to understand the SIOP Model as one model of sheltered instruction.
- Recognize that there are eight components and thirty aligned features that comprise the SIOP Model.

Language:

- Discuss orally one key point about each of eight specified factors that affect second language acquisition.
- Convert, in writing, a context-reduced task into a context-embedded academic task.
- Recognize that there are eight components and thirty aligned features that comprise the SIOP Model through reading, observation of video, and oral discussion.
- Orally state what you believe to be the two most important features of each component in the context of your classroom and explain why.

Afternoon Objectives

Content:

- Distinguish between content and language objectives.
- Review research that pertains to the importance of developing English learners' key vocabulary.
- Identify at least one technique for making explicit links to students' background experiences and between new concepts and past learning.

Language:

- Explain orally the relationship between content and language objectives.
- Apply knowledge of objectives by writing at least one content and one language objective.
- Discuss orally and list at least one technique for making explicit links to students' background experiences and between new concepts and past learning.
- Use the SIOP protocol to recognize, analyze, and rate orally the implementation of Building Background features depicted in a video clip of a classroom lesson.

Second Language Acquisition Theories

ERIC Digest

September 2000
EDO-FL-00-05

See other ERIC Digests on second language learning.

Contextual Factors in Second Language Acquisition

Aída Walqui, West Ed, San Francisco, California

While many discussions about learning a second language focus on teaching methodologies, little emphasis is given to the contextual factors — individual, social, and societal — that affect students' learning. These contextual factors can be considered from the perspective of the language, the learner, and the learning process. This digest discusses these perspectives as they relate to learning any second language, with a particular focus on how they affect adolescent learners of English as a second language.

Language

Several factors related to students' first and second languages shape their second language learning. These factors include the linguistic distance between the two languages, students' level of proficiency in the native language and their knowledge of the second language, the dialect of the native language spoken by the students (i.e., whether it is standard or nonstandard), the relative status of the students' language in the community, and societal attitudes toward the students' native language.

Language distance

Specific languages can be more or less difficult to learn, depending on how different from or similar they are to the languages the learner already knows. At the Defense Language Institute in Monterey, California, for example, languages are placed in four categories depending on their average learning difficulty from the perspective of a native English speaker. The basic intensive language course, which brings a student to an intermediate level, can be as short as 24 weeks for languages such as Dutch or Spanish, which are Indo European languages and use the same writing system as English, or as long as 65 weeks for languages such as Arabic, Korean, or Vietnamese, which are members of other language families and use different writing systems.

Native language proficiency

The student's level of proficiency in the native language — including not only oral language and literacy, but also metalinguistic development, training in formal and academic features of language use, and knowledge of rhetorical patterns and variations in genre and style — affects acquisition of a second language. The more academically sophisticated the student's native language knowledge and abilities, the easier it will be for that student to learn a second language. This helps explain why foreign exchange students tend to be successful in American high school classes: They already have high school level proficiency in their native language.

Knowledge of the second language

Students' prior knowledge of the second language is of course a significant factor in their current learning. High school students learning English as a second language in a U.S. classroom may possess skills ranging from conversational fluency acquired from contacts with the English-speaking world to formal knowledge obtained in English as a foreign language classes in their countries of origin. The extent and type of prior knowledge is an essential consideration in planning instruction. For example, a student with informal conversational English skills may have little understanding of English grammatical systems and may need specific instruction in English grammar.

Dialect and register

Learners may need to learn a dialect and a formal register in school that are different from those they encounter in their daily lives. This involves acquiring speech patterns that may differ significantly from those they are familiar with and value as members of a particular social group or speech community.

Language status

Consideration of dialects and registers of a language and of the relationships between two languages includes the relative prestige of different languages and dialects and of the cultures and ethnic groups associated with them. Students whose first language has a low status vis a vis the second may lose their first language, perhaps feeling they have to give up their own linguistic and cultural background to join the more prestigious society associated with the target language.

Language attitudes

Language attitudes in the learner, the peer group, the school, the neighborhood, and society at large can have an enormous effect on the second language learning process, both positive and negative. It is vital that teachers and students examine and understand these attitudes. In particular, they need to understand that learning a second language does not mean giving up one's first language or dialect. Rather, it involves adding a new language or dialect to one's repertoire.

This is true even for students engaged in formal study of their first language. For example, students in Spanish for native speakers classes may feel bad when teachers tell them that the ways they speak Spanish are not right. Clearly, this is an issue of dialect difference. School (in this case, classroom Spanish) requires formal registers and standard dialects, while conversation with friends and relatives may call for informal registers and nonstandard dialects. If their ways of talking outside of school are valued when used in appropriate contexts, students are more likely to be open to learning a new language or dialect, knowing that the new discourses will expand their communicative repertoires rather than displace their familiar ways of communicating.

The Learner

Students come from diverse backgrounds and have diverse needs and goals. With adolescent language learners, factors such as peer pressure, the presence of role models, and the level of home support can strongly affect the desire and ability to learn a second language.

Diverse needs

A basic educational principle is that new learning should be based on prior experiences and existing skills. Although this principle is known and generally agreed upon by educators, in practice it is often overshadowed by the administrative convenience of the linear curriculum and the single textbook. Homogeneous curricula and materials are problematic enough if all learners are from a single language and cultural background, but they are indefensible given the great diversity in today's classrooms. Such diversity requires a different conception of curricula and a different approach to materials. Differentiation and individualization are not a luxury in this context: They are a necessity.

Diverse goals

Learners' goals may determine how they use the language being learned, how native-like their pronunciation will be, how lexically elaborate and grammatically accurate their utterances will be, and how much energy they will expend to understand messages in the target language. Learners' goals can vary from wholly integrative — the desire to assimilate and become a full member of the English-speaking world — to primarily instrumental — oriented toward specific goals such as academic or professional success (Gardner, 1989). Educators working with English language learners must also consider whether the communities in which their students live, work, and study accept them, support their efforts, and offer them genuine English-learning opportunities.

Peer groups

Teenagers tend to be heavily influenced by their peer groups. In second language learning, peer pressure often undermines the goals set by parents and teachers. Peer pressure often reduces the desire of the student to work toward native pronunciation, because the sounds of the target language may be regarded as strange. For learners of English as a second language, speaking like a native speaker may unconsciously be regarded as a sign of no longer belonging to their native-language peer group. In working with secondary school students, it is important to keep these peer influences in mind and to foster a positive image for proficiency in a second language.

Role models

Students need to have positive and realistic role models who demonstrate the value of being proficient in more than one language. It is also helpful for students to read literature about the personal experiences of people from diverse language and dialect backgrounds. Through discussions of the challenges experienced by others, students can develop a better understanding of their own challenges.

Home support

Support from home is very important for successful second language learning. Some educators believe that parents of English language learners should speak only English in the home (see, e.g., recommendations made in Rodriguez, 1982). However, far more important than speaking English is that parents value both the native language and English, communicate with their children in whichever language is most comfortable, and show support for and interest in their children's progress.

The Learning Process

When we think of second language development as a learning process, we need to remember that different students have different learning styles, that intrinsic motivation aids learning, and that the quality of classroom interaction matters a great deal.

Learning styles

Research has shown that individuals vary greatly in the ways they learn a second language (Skehan, 1989). Some learners are more analytically oriented and thrive on picking apart words and sentences. Others are more globally oriented, needing to experience overall patterns of language in meaningful contexts before making sense of the linguistic parts and forms. Some learners are more visually oriented, others more geared to sounds.

Motivation

According to Deci and Ryan (1985), intrinsic motivation is related to basic human needs for competence, autonomy, and relatedness. Intrinsically motivated activities are those that the learner engages in for their own sake because of their value, interest, and challenge. Such activities present the best possible opportunities for learning.

Classroom interaction

Language learning does not occur as a result of the transmission of facts about language or from a succession of rote memorization drills. It is the result of opportunities for meaningful interaction with others in the target language. Therefore, lecturing and recitation are not the most appropriate modes of language use in the second language classroom. Teachers need to move toward more richly interactive language use, such as that found in instructional conversations (Tharp & Gallimore, 1988) and collaborative classroom work (Adger, Kalyanpur, Peterson, & Bridger, 1995).

Conclusion

While this digest has focused on the second language acquisition process from the perspective of the language, the learner, and the learning process, it is important to point out that the larger social and cultural contexts of second language development have a tremendous impact on second language learning, especially for immigrant students. The status of students' ethnic groups in relation to the larger culture can help or hinder the acquisition of the language of mainstream society.

References

Adger, C., Kalyanpur, M., Peterson, D., & Bridger, T. (1995). *Engaging students: Thinking, talking, cooperating.* Thousand Oaks, CA: Corwin.

Deci, E.L., & Ryan, R.M. (1985). *Intrinsic motivation and self-determination in human behavior.* New York: Plenum.

Gardner, H. (1989). *To open minds: Chinese clues to the dilemma of contemporary education.* New York: Basic.

Rodriguez, R. (1982). *Hunger of memory: The education of Richard Rodriguez, an autobiography.* Toronto: Bantam.

Skehan, P. (1989). *Individual differences in second-language learning.* London: Edward Arnold.

Tharp, R.G., & Gallimore, R. (1988). *Rousing minds to life: Teaching, learning, and school in social context.* New York: Cambridge University Press.

This digest is drawn from *Access and Engagement: Program Design and Instructional Approaches for Immigrant Students in Secondary Schools,* by Aída Walqui, the fourth volume in the Topics in Immigrant Education series. ERIC Document Reproduction Service No. EDO-FL-00-05. September 2000. Reprinted with permission.

This digest was prepared with funding from the U.S. Dept. of Education, Office of Educational Research and Improvement, National Library of Education, under contract no. ED-99-CO-0008. The opinions expressed do not necessarily reflect the positions or policies of ED, OERI, or NLE.

ERIC Clearinghouse on Languages and Linguistics
4646 40th Street, NW
Washington, DC 20016-1859
(202)362-0700 / (800)276-9834
eric@cal.org

How Does Each Factor Affect Second Language Acquisition?

As you carousel share around the room, identify one key point for each factor.

Motivation

____

____

____

____

Age

____

____

____

____

Personality and learning style

____

____

____

____

Peers and role models

____

____

____

____

Quality of instruction

First language development

Access to the language/language distance

Language attitude and status

Classroom Connections: Carousel Sharing

Could you use carousel sharing in your classroom? If so, how?

Why would it be beneficial to English learners?

Key Words in Understanding Cummins' Theory

- **Context-Embedded:** Provides many cues for the learner to access information (realia, video, plays, illustrations).
- **Context-Reduced:** Learner must rely on language to access information (lecture, reading a text, worksheets).
- **Cognitively Demanding:** Learner must have enough background knowledge to scaffold new ideas that are academically challenging.
  - — Higher levels of Bloom's Taxonomy: Synthesis and Evaluation
  - — For example, "What predictions can you make based on the data?"
- **Cognitively Undemanding:** Language required is social and not specialized.
  - — Lower level of Bloom's Taxonomy: Knowledge and Comprehension
  - — For example, "What time is it?"

(Cummins, J., 1981)

Cummins' Model of Academic Language (1981)

BICS	CALP
Basic Interpersonal Communication Skills	Cognitive Academic Language Proficiency

Cummins' Model of Academic Language (1981)

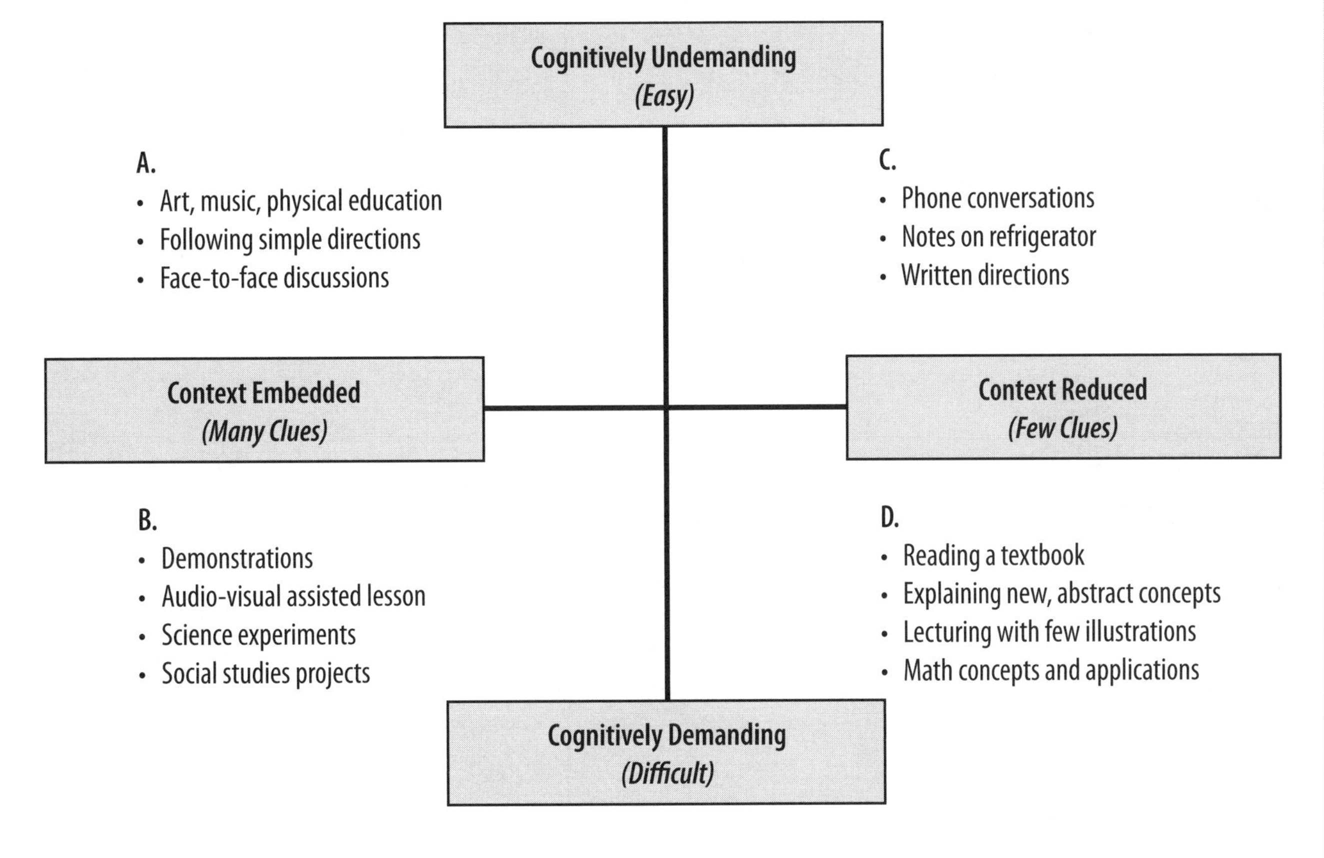

1 2 3 4 5 6 7 8 9 10 11 12

(Cummins, J., 1981)

Cummins' Model of Academic Language

	Context-Embedded	Context-Reduced
Cognitively Undemanding	A	C
Cognitively Demanding	B	D

Organize your activities to match Cummins' quadrants. Be ready to share in 2 minutes.

Converting Academic Tasks from D to B

Think of an activity from your own classroom that fits into quadrant D.

What steps did you take to convert the context-reduced task to a context-embedded academic task (from quadrant D to B)? Be sure to keep the cognitive demand.

Second Language Acquisition Theories: Session Reflection

What questions do you have about this session?

What was the most significant and useful new learning that you gained through this session?

Explain why.

Introduction to Sheltered Instruction and the SIOP® Model

2
3
4
5
6
7
8
9
10
11
12

Content and Language Teachers

What are the similarities and differences between a language teacher (English, EL, and language arts) and a content teacher (math, science, social studies, and electives)?

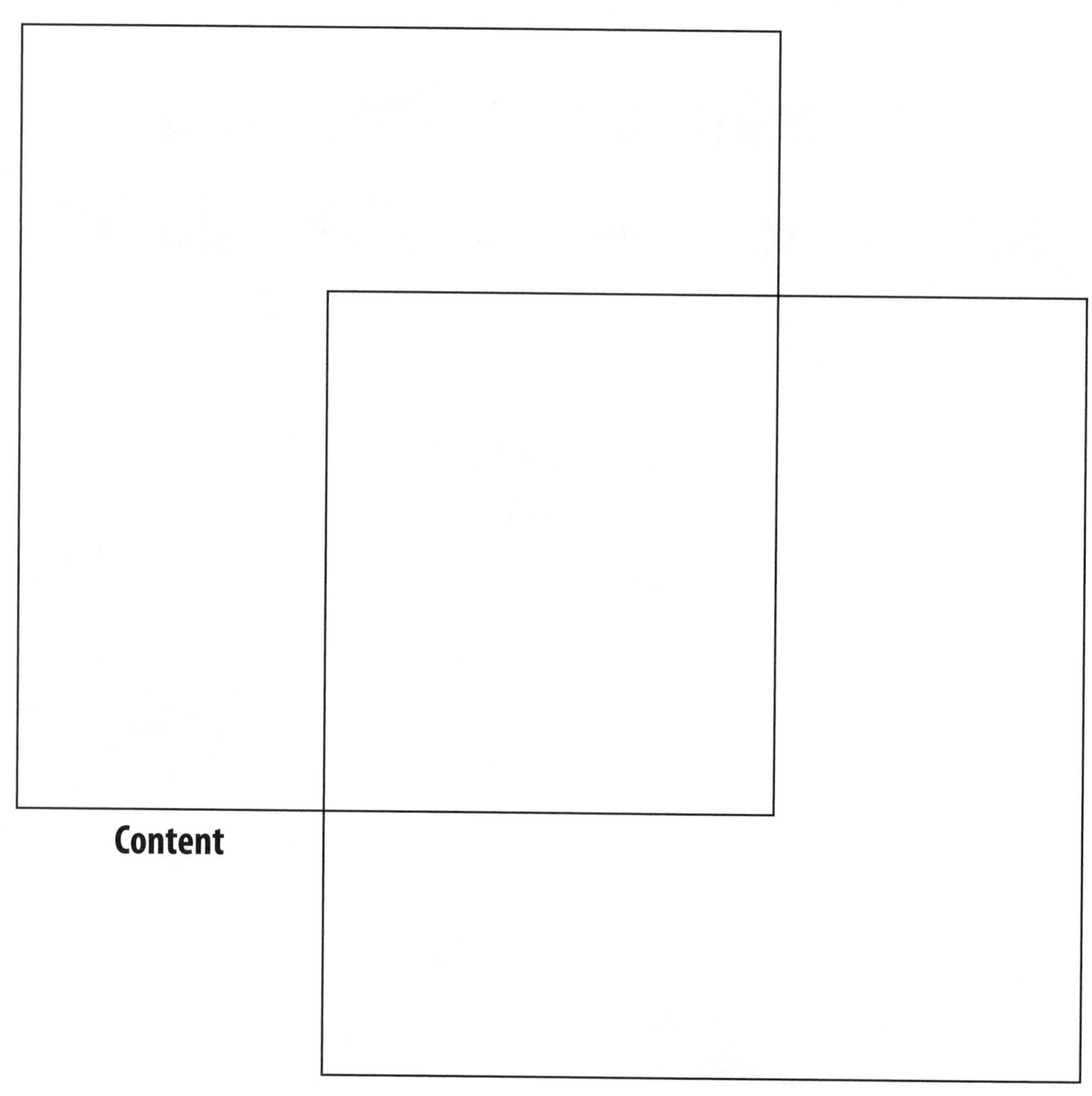

From Short, D., Hudec, J., and Echevarria, J. (2002).

What Is Sheltered Instruction?

Write your definition of sheltered instruction below.

Introduction to the SIOP Model

1. Has the SIOP Model been shown to be effective through scientifically-based research? If so, how?

2. What is one point you found interesting in the video?

The Sheltered Instruction Observation Protocol (SIOP®)

(Echevarria, Vogt, & Short, 2000; 2004; 2008)

Observer(s): ____________ Teacher: ____________
Date: ____________ School: ____________
Grade: ____________ Class/Topic: ____________
ESL Level: ____________ Lesson: Multi-day Single-day *(circle one)*

Total Points Possible: 120 (Subtract 4 points for each NA given)
Total Points Earned: ________ Percentage Score: ________

Directions: *Check the number that best reflects what you observe in a SIOP® lesson. You may give a score from 0-4 (or NA on selected items). Cite under "Comments" specific examples of the behaviors observed.*

	Highly Evident		Somewhat Evident		Not Evident	
I. Lesson Preparation	4	3	2	1	0	
1. **Content objectives** clearly defined, displayed, and reviewed with students	❑	❑	❑	❑	❑	
2. **Language objectives** clearly defined, displayed, and reviewed with students	❑	❑	❑	❑	❑	
3. **Content concepts** appropriate for age and educational background level of students	❑	❑	❑	❑	❑	
4. **Supplementary materials** used to a high degree, making the lesson clear and meaningful (e.g., computer programs, graphs, models, visuals)	❑	❑	❑	❑	❑	
5. **Adaptation of content** (e.g., text, assignment) to all levels of student proficiency	❑	❑	❑	❑	❑	**NA**
6. **Meaningful activities** that integrate lesson concepts (e.g., interviews, letter writing, simulations, models) with language practice opportunities for reading, writing, listening, and/or speaking	❑	❑	❑	❑	❑	
Comments:						
2. Building Background	4	3	2	1	0	
7. **Concepts explicitly linked** to students' background experiences	❑	❑	❑	❑	❑	**NA**
8. **Links explicitly made** between past learning and new concepts	❑	❑	❑	❑	❑	
9. **Key vocabulary** emphasized (e.g., introduced, written, repeated, and highlighted for students to see)	❑	❑	❑	❑	❑	
Comments:						
3. Comprehensible Input	4	3	2	1	0	
10. **Speech** appropriate for students' proficiency levels (e.g., slower rate, enunciation, and simple sentence structure for beginners)	❑	❑	❑	❑	❑	
11. **Clear explanation** of academic tasks	❑	❑	❑	❑	❑	
12. **A variety of techniques** used to make content concepts clear (e.g., modeling, visuals, hands-on activities, demonstrations, gestures, body language)	❑	❑	❑	❑	❑	
Comments:						
4. Strategies	4	3	2	1	0	
13. Ample opportunities provided for students to use **learning strategies**	❑	❑	❑	❑	❑	

	Highly Evident		Somewhat Evident		Not Evident	
14. **Scaffolding techniques** consistently used, assisting and supporting student understanding (e.g., think-alouds)	❑	❑	❑	❑	❑	
15. A variety of **questions or tasks that promote higher-order thinking skills** (e.g., literal, analytical, and interpretive questions)	❑	❑	❑	❑	❑	

Comments:

5. Interaction	**4**	**3**	**2**	**1**	**0**	
16. Frequent opportunities for **interaction** and discussion between teacher/student and among students, which encourage elaborated responses about lesson concepts	❑	❑	❑	❑	❑	
17. **Grouping configurations** support language and content objectives of the lesson	❑	❑	❑	❑	❑	
18. Sufficient **wait time for student responses** consistently provided	❑	❑	❑	❑	❑	
19. Ample opportunities for students to **clarify key concepts in Ll** as needed with aide, peer, or L1 text	❑	❑	❑	❑	❑	**NA**

Comments:

6. Practice and Application	**4**	**3**	**2**	**1**	**0**	
20. **Hands-on materials and/or manipulatives** provided for students to practice using new content knowledge	❑	❑	❑	❑	❑	**NA**
21. Activities provided for students to **apply content and language knowledge** in the classroom	❑	❑	❑	❑	❑	**NA**
22. Activities integrate all **language skills** (i.e., reading, writing, listening, and speaking)	❑	❑	❑	❑	❑	

Comments:

7. Lesson Delivery	**4**	**3**	**2**	**1**	**0**
23. **Content objectives** clearly supported by lesson delivery	❑	❑	❑	❑	❑
24. **Language objectives** clearly supported by lesson delivery	❑	❑	❑	❑	❑
25. **Students engaged** approximately 90% to 100% of the period	❑	❑	❑	❑	❑
26. **Pacing** of the lesson appropriate to students' ability levels	❑	❑	❑	❑	❑

Comments:

8. Review and Assessment	**4**	**3**	**2**	**1**	**0**
27. Comprehensive **review of key vocabulary**	❑	❑	❑	❑	❑
28. Comprehensive **review of key content concepts**	❑	❑	❑	❑	❑
29. Regular **feedback** provided to students on their output (e.g., language, content, work)	❑	❑	❑	❑	❑
30. **Assessment of student comprehension and learning** of all lesson objectives (e.g., spot checking, group response) throughout the lesson	❑	❑	❑	❑	❑

Comments:

SIOP Model Component Preview

Lesson Preparation

What do you believe are the two most important features for your context and students? Why?

Building Background

What do you believe are the two most important features for your context and students? Why?

Comprehensible Input

What do you believe are the two most important features for your context and students? Why?

Strategies

What do you believe are the two most important features for your context and students? Why?

Interaction

What do you believe are the two most important features for your context and students? Why?

2 3 4 5 6 7 8 9 10 11 12

Practice and Application

What do you believe are the two most important features for your context and students? Why?

Lesson Delivery

What do you believe are the two most important features for your context and students? Why?

Review and Assessment

What do you believe are the two most important features for your context and students? Why?

Introduction to Sheltered Instruction and the SIOP Model: Wrap-Up

Write down reasons or examples of how the SIOP Model will help to support quality instruction at your school.

Introduction to Sheltered Instruction and the SIOP Model: Session Reflection

What questions do you have about this session?

What are one or two key ideas presented that you believe are most significant or useful to your teaching of English learners?

Explain why.

Lesson Preparation

Lesson Preparation Features

1. **Content objectives** clearly defined, displayed, and reviewed with students

2. **Language objectives** clearly defined, displayed, and reviewed with students

3. **Content concepts** appropriate for age and educational background level of students

4. **Supplementary materials** used to a high degree, making the lesson clear and meaningful

5. **Adaptation of content** to all levels of student proficiency

6. **Meaningful activities** that integrate lesson concepts with language practice opportunities for reading, writing, listening, and/or speaking

What Are Language Objectives?

Why might language objectives be important for English learners?

3

4

5

6

7

8

9

10

11

12

Lesson Preparation
T-Chart

Content Objective	Language Objective

Considerations for Language Objectives

1. Key content vocabulary

____

____

____

2. Language skills

____

____

____

3. Grammar and language structure

____

____

____

4. Tasks (activities)

____

____

____

5. Language learning strategies

____

____

____

Matching Content and Language Objectives

How do these objectives work together to help students meet this standard?

Math: Determine the equivalence among decimals, fractions, and percents.

Science: Differentiate between plant and animal cells.

Writing: Write a narrative that includes:

a main idea based on real or imagined events
b. character(s)
c. a sequence of events

Social Studies: Construct various timelines of key events, people, and periods of the historical era being studied.

Reading: Use reading strategies (e.g., drawing conclusions, determining cause and effect, making inferences, sequencing) to comprehend text.

Let's Write Objectives

Subject________________ Grade Level_____

Lesson Concept:

____

____

____

____

Content Objective:

____

____

____

____

Language Objective:

____

____

____

____

Meaningful activity that helps meet the above objectives:

____

____

____

____

Classroom Connections: Inside/Outside Circle

Could you use the inside/outside circle in your classroom? If so, how?

How does it support language development for all learners?

Lesson Preparation: Session Reflection

What questions do you have about this session?

What key ideas, learnings, and insights from this session will be most useful in helping your English learners comprehend the content you present to them?

Explain why.

Please answer the prompts in the Lesson Preparation section of the SIOP Model Self-Assessment on page 149 of this workbook.

Building Background

4
5
6
7
8
9
10
11
12

Building Background Features

7. **Concepts explicitly linked** to students' background experiences

8. **Links explicitly made** between past learning and new concepts

9. **Key vocabulary** emphasized

Making Explicit Links to Students' Background Experiences and Past Learning

How do you make explicit links to students' background experiences in your classroom?

How do you make explicit links between new concepts and past learning?

Ways to Link New Knowledge to Past Learning and Background Experiences

- **Questioning Strategies:** Ask explicit questions. "Who remembers what we learned about___?" "How does that relate to what we are now going to learn?"

- **Charts/Reference Points:** Outlines, maps, graphic organizers, and word walls/banks that include key information that has been studied or is being studied.

- **KWL:** What do you already know? What do you want to know? What have you learned?

- **Student Journals:** Have students write a journal entry about their own personal experiences with the topic.

- **Quick-Writes:** Have students quickly write a short response or summary about what they have learned or still have questions about.

Emphasizing Key Vocabulary: What Techniques Have You Observed or Used in Your Classroom?

List techniques that you've used in your classroom.

Vocabulary words appropriate for a specific content area you teach (English, social studies, math, science):

Describe a technique or strategy to emphasize the five vocabulary words above.

Content Objective:

Language Objective:

Ways to Emphasize Key Vocabulary

- **Vocabulary Word Maps:** Students define the word in their own words, identify a synonym for the word, write a sentence in meaningful context, and draw a picture.

- **Tired Daisy:** Students identify synonyms for common words that are used over and over again, completing the figure of a flower. The goal is to expose students to many words as they are focusing on learning and applying individual words.

- **Concept Definition Map:** Students apply content vocabulary by creating a graphic organizer that identifies what the word is, lists examples of how the word is used or applied in context, and gives other ideas of what the word is like.

- **Word Walls:** Word walls provide students with a reference point of key terms related to a certain topic or theme. Students are responsible for writing and illustrating the words posted on the word wall and should be referred back to them as often as possible.

- **Personal Dictionaries:** Students identify and list words, creating a personal vocabulary resource.

- **Word Sorts:** Students categorize and/or organize words or phrases based on meaning, structure, sounds, or content relationships.

- **Word Study Books:** Students make personal books listing and defining frequently used words and concepts.

From Echevarria, J., Vogt, M.E., and Short, D. (2008). *Making content comprehensible for English learners: The SIOP Model.* 3rd ed. Boston, MA: Pearson Allyn and Bacon, pp. 63–68.

Building Background: Evaluating a Classroom Lesson

As you observe the classroom video, note evidence that you see and hear of any of the Building Background features being incorporated into this portion of the lesson.

4
5
6
7
8
9
10
11
12

After watching the video, please respond to these questions:

- How are *concepts explicitly linked to students' background experiences*?

- How are *links explicitly made between past learning and new concepts*?

- How is *key vocabulary emphasized*?

- Were there missed opportunities where the teacher could have built additional background?

Building Background Ratings

BUILDING BACKGROUND

4	3	2	1	0	NA

7. **Concepts explicitly linked** to students' background experiences

Concepts loosely linked to students' background experiences

Concepts not explicitly linked to students' background experiences

Comments:

4	3	2	1	0

8. **Links explicitly made** between past learning and new concepts

Few links made between past learning and new concepts

No links made between past learning and new concepts

Comments:

4	3	2	1	0

9. **Key vocabulary** emphasized (e.g., introduced, written, repeated, and highlighted for students to see)

Key vocabulary introduced, but not emphasized

Key vocabulary not introduced or emphasized

Comments:

From Echevarria, J., Vogt, M.E., and Short, D. (2008). *Making content comprehensible for English learners: The SIOP® Model.* (3rd ed.) Boston, MA: Pearson Allyn and Bacon, pp. 222–227.

How could the use of one or more features have been improved in the lesson?

Building Background: Wrap-Up

- I learned . . .

- I began to wonder . . .

- I practiced . . .

- I felt . . .

- I thought . . .

- I understood . . .

Building Background: Session Reflection

What questions do you have about this session?

What key ideas, learnings, and insights from this session will be most useful in helping your English learners comprehend the content you present to them?

Explain why.

Please answer the prompts in the Building Background section of the SIOP Model Self-Assessment on page 149 of this workbook.

Day 2

Day 2
Content and Language Objectives

Morning Objectives

Content:

- Recognize and gain a basic understanding of the three features of the Comprehensible Input component.
- Understand three different types of learning strategies—metacognitive, cognitive, and social/affective—and how they promote student autonomy.
- Identify at least three purposes for asking higher-level thinking questions to students of all language proficiency levels.
- Identify at least one technique to scaffold students' verbal, procedural, and instructional understanding.

Language:

- Reflect, in writing, and share orally the methods you currently use in your own classroom for making content comprehensible.
- Analyze the use of the features of Comprehensible Input in teaching scenarios by reading vignettes and orally discussing and justifying assigned ratings.
- Practice writing a set of questions that incorporates higher levels of thinking about one topic.
- Use the SIOP protocol to recognize, analyze, and rate orally the implementation of Strategies features depicted in a video clip of a classroom lesson.

Afternoon Objectives

Content:

- Understand the purpose and value of balanced linguistic exchanges and interactions between teachers and English learners in the classroom.
- Explain at least three ways that various grouping configurations can support the content and language objectives of a lesson.
- Identify three reasons why practicing and applying content and language knowledge is important for English learners.
- Generate ideas for applying content and language knowledge by planning and acting out a hands-on technique.

(Continued on next page)

Language:

- Write a list on note cards of at least five different ways to create opportunities for classroom student interaction and orally share ideas in a conga line.
- Use the SIOP protocol to recognize, analyze, and rate orally the implementation of Interaction features depicted in a video clip of a classroom lesson.
- List, in writing, and share orally at least five ways you can create opportunities for your students to practice and apply content and language knowledge with English learners in your classroom.
- Use the SIOP protocol to recognize, analyze, and rate orally the implementation of Practice and Application features depicted in a video clip of a classroom lesson.

Comprehensible Input

5
6
7
8
9
10
11
12

Wright Family Exercise

Each time the word Wright or right is read, pass the object to the right. Each time the word left is read, pass the object to the left.

Mrs. Wright eyed her grocery list carefully. "There won't be anything left of our budget after shopping" she said. Mr. Wright looked up from his paper and said: "That's all right my dear, if there isn't anything left, I'll be happy if the Wright family makes it through the month."

As Mr. Wright turned back to his paper he said, "Have you the right gift for Sue Wright's birthday? She's been pretty lonely since her daughter left home right after she married. Uncle Tom left her a lot of money, but she does not enjoy life right."

Son, Ed Wright, was studying in the corner of the left side of the fireplace. "I wish Sue Wright would ask me the right way to spend the money."

Mary Wright said, "she would not have much left if she did. Your weekly allowance is gone before you get it right in your hands."

"And I suppose you have all yours left Miss Mary," said Ed Wright.

"I don't have it all left but I have enough left to buy toys I like," Mary Wright said.

Just then the doorbell rang. Mary Wright ran to answer the door, and the postman left a special delivery letter for the Wright family. She took it to Father Wright and he opened it. Inside was a letter and four new ten dollar bills. Mr. Wright shouted, "It's from Aunt Wright saying she has left town and decided to go right to her daughter's house."

"Say, she's all right" shouted Eddie Wright.

"Bless her heart," said Mother Wright.

"How wonderful of her," said Mary Wright.

"It makes each of us right happy to think she wrote us before she left," declared Father Wright. "At least it's all right with the Wright family."

What was the passage about?

How did you feel as the passage was read?

What could the reader have done differently to help you comprehend the content of the passage?

Comprehensible Input Features

10. **Speech** appropriate for students' proficiency levels

11. **Clear explanation** of academic tasks

12. **A variety of techniques** used to make content concepts clear

Techniques for Making Input Comprehensible

Write one of the following letters to indicate the frequency with which you use the teaching techniques below.

A if you do it all the time

M if you do it most of the time

R if you rarely do it

_____ Use expression and body language.

_____ Speak slowly and clearly.

_____ Use more pauses between phrases.

_____ Use shorter sentences with simpler syntax.

_____ Stress high-frequency vocabulary.

_____ Repeat and review vocabulary.

_____ Watch carefully for comprehension and be ready to repeat or restate to clarify meaning whenever necessary.

_____ Be friendly and enthusiastic.

_____ Maintain a warm, supportive affect.

_____ Open discussion to different perspectives of a topic.

5 6 7 8 9 10 11 12

Comprehensible Input: Evaluating a Lesson Vignette

- Did the teacher incorporate *speech appropriate for students' proficiency levels* in his/her lesson? If so, how? If not, how could this have been improved?

- Did the teacher model *clear explanation of academic tasks*? If so, how? If not, how could this have been improved?

- Did the teacher incorporate *a variety of techniques used to make content concepts clear*? If so, how? If not, how could this have been improved?

Comprehensible Input Ratings

COMPREHENSIBLE INPUT				
4	3	2	1	0
10. **Speech** appropriate for students' proficiency levels (e.g., slower rate, enunciation, and simple sentence structure for beginners)		**Speech** sometimes inappropriate for students' proficiency levels		**Speech** inappropriate for students' proficiency levels
Comments:				
4	3	2	1	0
11. **Clear explanation** of academic tasks		**Unclear** explanation of academic tasks		**No** explanation of academic tasks
Comments:				
4	3	2	1	0
12. **A variety of techniques** used to make content concepts clear (e.g., modeling, visuals, hands-on activities, demonstrations, gestures, body language)		Some **techniques** used to make content concepts clear		No **techniques** used to make content concepts clear
Comments:				

From Echevarria, J., Vogt, M.E., and Short, D. (2008). *Making content comprehensible for English learners: The SIOP® Model.* (3rd ed.) Boston, MA: Pearson Allyn and Bacon, pp. 222–227.

How could the use of one or more features have been improved in the lesson?

Comprehensible Input: Wrap-Up

What do you believe you already do to make input comprehensible for English learners?

What have you not tried yet, but might be useful for your students?

Comprehensible Input: Session Reflection

What questions do you have about this session?

What key ideas, learnings, and insights from this session will be most useful in helping your English learners comprehend the content you present to them?

Explain why.

Please answer the prompts in the Comprehensible Input section of the SIOP Model Self-Assessment on page 149 of this workbook.

Strategies

6
7
8
9
10
11
12

Strategies Features

13. Ample opportunities provided for students to use **learning strategies**

14. **Scaffolding techniques** consistently used, assisting and supporting student understanding

15. A variety of **questions or tasks that promote higher-order thinking skills**

Creating Higher-Order Thinking Questions

Think of a knowledge-level question about something you've taught recently and write it below. Then, write three related questions that demand higher levels of thinking.

Related higher-level thinking question:

Explain/describe the kind of thinking this question requires students to do.

Related higher-level thinking question:

Explain/describe the kind of thinking this question requires students to do.

Related higher-level thinking question:

Explain/describe the kind of thinking this question requires students to do.

Strategies: Evaluating a Video Lesson

As you observe the classroom video, note evidence that you see and hear of any of the Strategies features being incorporated into this portion of the lesson.

After watching the video, please respond to these questions:

- How were *ample opportunities provided for students to use learning strategies*?

- In what ways were *scaffolding techniques consistently used to assist and support student understanding*?

- How were *a variety of questions or tasks that promote higher-order thinking skills* implemented?

Strategies Ratings

STRATEGIES

4	3	2	1	0
13. Ample opportunities provided for students to use **learning strategies**		Inadequate opportunities provided for students to use **learning strategies**		No opportunity provided for students to use **learning strategies**

Comments:

4	3	2	1	0
14. **Scaffolding techniques** consistently used, assisting and supporting student understanding (e.g., think-alouds)		**Scaffolding techniques** occasionally used		**Scaffolding techniques** not used

Comments:

4	3	2	1	0
15. A variety of **questions or tasks that promote higher-order thinking skills** (e.g., literal, analytical, and interpretive questions)		Infrequent **questions or tasks that promote higher-order thinking skills**		No **questions or tasks that promote higher-order thinking skills**

Comments:

From Echevarria, J., Vogt, M.E., and Short, D. (2008). *Making content comprehensible for English learners: The SIOP® Model.* (3rd ed.) Boston, MA: Pearson Allyn and Bacon, pp. 222–227.

How could the use of one or more features have been improved in the lesson?

Strategies: Session Reflection

What questions do you have about this session?

What key ideas, learnings, and insights from this session will be most useful in helping your English learners comprehend the content you present to them?

Explain why.

Please answer the prompts in the Strategies section of the SIOP Model Self-Assessment on page 149 of this workbook.

Interaction

7
8
9
10
11
12

Classroom Connections: Conga Line

Could you use the conga line in your classroom? If so, how?

How does it support language development for all learners?

Interaction Features

16. Frequent opportunities for **interaction** and discussion between teacher/student and among students, which encourage elaborated responses about lesson concepts

17. **Grouping configurations** support language and content objectives of the lesson

18. Sufficient **wait time for student responses** consistently provided

19. Ample opportunities for students to **clarify key concepts in L1** as needed with aide, peer, or L1 text

Analyzing Content Clarification for ELs

Read the Mainstream Lesson (pages 116–117) and the SIOP Model Lesson (pages 117–119) in *Making Content Comprehensible for English Learners*. Highlight or underline the questions that the teacher asks in each vignette. Then respond to the questions below.

In the Mainstream Lesson:

What do you notice about the kinds of opportunities that students were given to clarify their understanding of key concepts or vocabulary?

____

____

Describe the kinds of questions that the teacher used in the vignette.

____

____

In the SIOP Model Lesson:

Describe the kinds of questions that the teacher used to help students clarify their understanding of key concepts or vocabulary.

____

____

List three things that the teacher did to help students clarify their understanding and the effect of each action.

1. ____

Effect: ____

2. ____

Effect: ____

3. ____

Effect: ____

EL Grouping Configurations

Review these ideas about grouping configurations and respond to the questions below.

- Types of groups (random, voluntary, teacher-assigned)
- Changing groups (frequency, management)
- Group roles (determined by activity)
- Planning group activities (instructions and modeling)
- Configuration and activity must follow the objective

1. Identify the types of grouping configurations we have used so far in this program.
2. Choose three ideas from the list of grouping configurations and write an explanation for how each could support content and language objectives for ELs.

Idea: ______________________________

Explanation: ______________________________

____

____

____

Idea: ______________________________

Explanation: ______________________________

____

____

____

Idea: ______________________________

Explanation: ______________________________

____

____

____

Interaction: Evaluating a Video Lesson

- Were there *frequent opportunities for student/teacher interaction and discussion between teacher/student and among students?*

- How did *grouping configurations support the content and language objectives of the lesson?*

- Was *sufficient wait time for student responses* provided?

- Were *ample opportunities for students to clarify key concepts in L1 as needed with aide, peer, or L1 text* provided?

Interaction Ratings

INTERACTION

4	3	2	1	0	
16. Frequent opportunities for **interaction** and discussion between teacher/student and among students, which encourage elaborated responses about lesson concepts		**Interaction** mostly teacher-dominated with some opportunities for students to talk about or question lesson concepts		**Interaction** teacher-dominated with no opportunities for students to discuss lesson concepts	

Comments:

4	3	2	1	0	
17. **Grouping configurations** support language and content objectives of the lesson		**Grouping configurations** unevenly support the language and content objectives		**Grouping configurations** do not support the language and content objectives	

Comments:

4	3	2	1	0	
18. Sufficient **wait time for student responses** consistently provided		Sufficient **wait time for student responses** occasionally provided		Sufficient **wait time for student responses** not provided	

Comments:

4	3	2	1	0	NA
19. Ample opportunities for students to **clarify key concepts in L1** as needed with aide, peer, or L1 text		Some opportunities for students to **clarify key concepts in L1**		No opportunities for students to **clarify key concepts in L1**	

Comments:

From Echevarria, J., Vogt, M.E., and Short, D. (2008). *Making content comprehensible for English learners: The SIOP® Model.* (3rd ed.) Boston, MA: Pearson Allyn and Bacon, pp. 222–227.

How could the use of one or more features have been improved in the lesson?

___

___

___

___

Interaction: Wrap-Up

Describe a class that integrates reading, writing, listening, and speaking.

What does it look like?	What does it sound like?
What does it feel like?	What are some examples or ideas?

From Short, D., Hudec, J., and Echevarria, J. (2002).

Interaction: Session Reflection

What questions do you have about this session?

What key ideas, learnings, and insights from this session will be most useful in helping your English learners comprehend the content you present to them?

Explain why.

Please answer the prompts in the Interaction section of the SIOP Model Self-Assessment on page 149 of this workbook.

Practice and Application

8
9
10
11
12

Practice and Application Features

20. **Hands-on materials and/or manipulatives** provided for students to practice using new content knowledge

21. Activities provided for students to **apply content and language knowledge** in the classroom

22. Activities integrate all **language skills** (i.e., reading, writing, listening, and speaking)

Guided Practice for ELs: Questions

1. How much material should be practiced at one time?

   Answer:____

   Notes: ____

2. How long should a practice period be?

   Answer:____

   Notes: ____

3. How often should students practice?

   Answer:____

   Notes: ____

4. How will students know how well they have done?

   Answer:____

   Notes: ____

Practice and Application: Evaluating a Video Lesson

Complete the three sections below while watching the video. Please focus on how the following features are supported:

- Provides hands-on materials and/or manipulatives for students to practice using new content knowledge
- Provides activities for students to apply content and language knowledge in the classroom
- Uses activities that integrate all language skills (i.e., reading, writing, listening, and speaking)

P: What did you view that was a **plus** or positive about using the features?	**I:** What did you view that was **interesting** about addressing the features?

Q: What **questions** do you have about the way the features were supported?

Practice and Application Ratings

PRACTICE AND APPLICATION

4	3	2	1	0	NA
20. **Hands-on materials and/or manipulatives** provided for students to practice using new content knowledge		Few **hands-on materials and/or manipulatives** provided for students to practice using new content knowledge		No **hands-on materials and/or manipulatives** provided for students to practice using new content knowledge	

Comments:

4	3	2	1	0	NA
21. Activities provided for students to **apply content and language knowledge** in the classroom		Activities provided for students to **apply** either **content or language knowledge** in the classroom		No activities provided for students to **apply content and language knowledge** in the classroom	

Comments:

4	3	2	1	0
22. Activities integrate all **language skills** (i.e., reading, writing, listening, and speaking)		Activities integrate some **language skills**		Activities do not integrate **language skills**

Comments:

From Echevarria, J., Vogt, M.E., and Short, D. (2008). *Making content comprehensible for English learners: The SIOP® Model.* (3rd ed.) Boston, MA: Pearson Allyn and Bacon, pp. 222–227.

How could the use of one or more features have been improved in the lesson?

___

___

___

___

___

___

___

___

___

___

Practice and Application: Session Reflection

What questions do you have about this session?

What key ideas, learnings, and insights from this session will be most useful in helping your English learners comprehend the content you present to them?

Explain why.

Please answer the prompts in the Practice and Application section of the SIOP Model Self-Assessment on page 150 of this workbook.

Practice and Application: Wrap-Up
Extra! Extra!

Write a headline that a reporter would write for an article about a key learning or realization from this training.

Use this page to write notes or ideas as you work with your group to plan the headline.

Day 3

Day 3
Content and Language Objectives

Morning Objectives

Content:

- Identify three lesson delivery challenges in your classroom.
- Explain how you might use content and language objectives more effectively in lesson delivery.
- Differentiate between assessment and evaluation by identifying the characteristics of each.

Language:

- Write words and phrases to complete a graphic organizer to represent at least six delivery practices that directly address your lesson delivery challenges.
- Use the SIOP protocol to recognize, analyze, and rate orally the use of Lesson Delivery features depicted in a video clip of a classroom lesson.
- Share Review and Assessment techniques you can use in your classroom by writing and sharing orally in a simultaneous roundtable activity.
- Analyze the relationship between the Review and Assessment features and the Effective Teaching Cycle for English Learners by writing a quick response and orally sharing ideas.

Afternoon Objectives

Content:

- Identify which SIOP components and features you are already implementing successfully in your classroom and which will be the most challenging to implement in your classroom.
- Select one or two components that you feel would be a good starting place for you to fully implement in your classroom.
- Develop a written lesson plan that begins to incorporate the eight SIOP components and focuses on implementing the features from at least one component to meet the learning needs of English learners in your classroom.

(Continued on next page)

Language:

- Collaborate with grade or subject-level colleagues to:
  - Select one or two components that you will focus on together and list in writing action steps you can take to implement the component in your school or district.
  - Discuss orally and list in writing ways you can support each other to sustain the implementation of the SIOP Model in your school or district.
- List up to three key questions or challenges you still have about implementing the SIOP Model in your district and list, in writing, ways that you can address them.
- Share your lesson plan by writing on chart paper and describe orally how three key features were incorporated into your lesson plan and the anticipated effect that they will have on the content comprehension of your ELs.

Lesson Delivery

9

10

11

12

Lesson Delivery Features

23. **Content objectives** clearly supported by lesson delivery

24. **Language objectives** clearly supported by lesson delivery

25. **Students engaged** approximately 90% to 100% of the period

26. **Pacing** of the lesson appropriate to students' ability levels

What Do You Think About Lesson Objectives?

1. Why is it necessary to tell the objectives to students at the beginning of a lesson?

2. Why is it a good idea to review the objectives at the end of each lesson?

3. What are some factors that contribute to high levels of student engagement?

4. How do objectives affect the pacing of a lesson?

9

10

11

12

How Do You Keep Students Engaged?

In pairs, think about how you engage students in your classrooms and/or new ideas you'd like to try. Then, individually write your ideas on the graphic organizer below. Be ready to share.

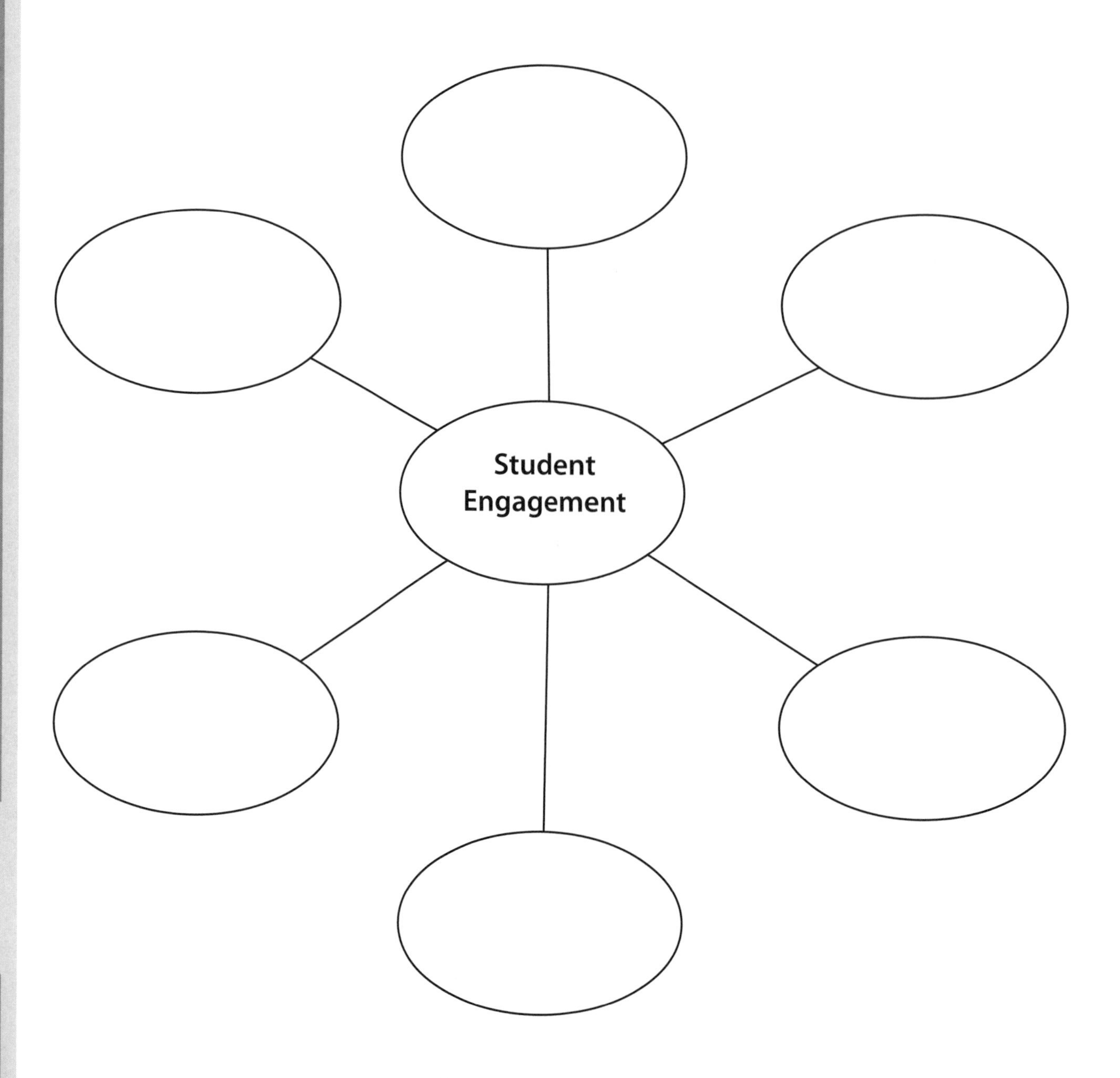

Factors Contributing to High Levels of Student Engagement

1. Well-planned lessons
2. Clear explanation of academic tasks or instruction
3. Appropriate amount of time spent on an academic task
4. Strong classroom management skills
5. Opportunities for students to apply learning in a meaningful way
6. Active student involvement
7. Lesson design meets the language and learning needs of students

Lesson Delivery: Evaluating a Lesson Vignette

- In what ways were the *content objectives clearly supported by lesson delivery*?

- In what ways were the *language objectives clearly supported by lesson delivery*?

- What methods were used to keep *students engaged approximately 90% to 100% of the period*?

- How did the teacher keep the *pacing of the lesson appropriate to the students' ability levels*?

Lesson Delivery Ratings

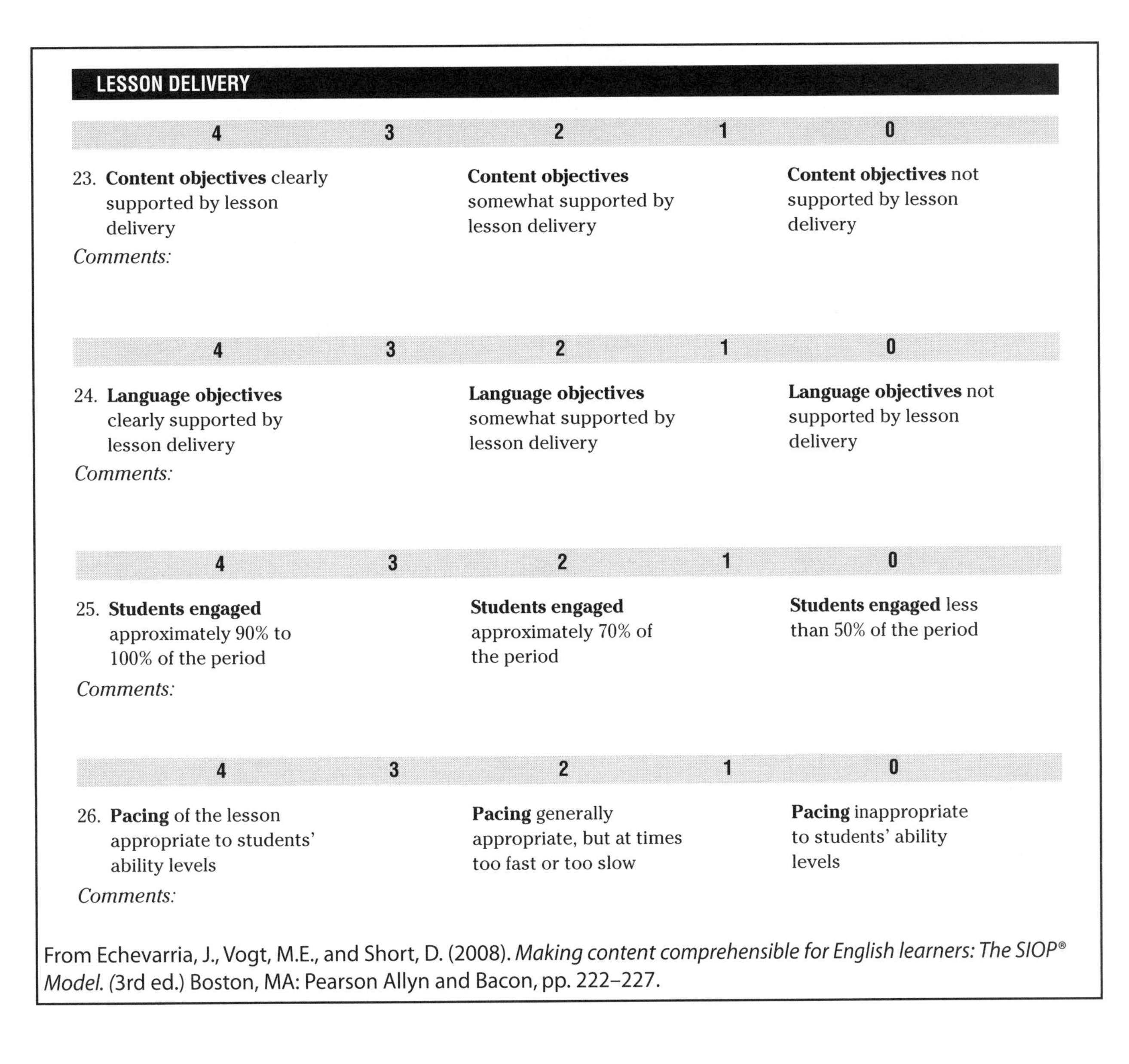

LESSON DELIVERY

4	3	2	1	0
23. **Content objectives** clearly supported by lesson delivery		**Content objectives** somewhat supported by lesson delivery		**Content objectives** not supported by lesson delivery

Comments:

4	3	2	1	0
24. **Language objectives** clearly supported by lesson delivery		**Language objectives** somewhat supported by lesson delivery		**Language objectives** not supported by lesson delivery

Comments:

4	3	2	1	0
25. **Students engaged** approximately 90% to 100% of the period		**Students engaged** approximately 70% of the period		**Students engaged** less than 50% of the period

Comments:

4	3	2	1	0
26. **Pacing** of the lesson appropriate to students' ability levels		**Pacing** generally appropriate, but at times too fast or too slow		**Pacing** inappropriate to students' ability levels

Comments:

From Echevarria, J., Vogt, M.E., and Short, D. (2008). *Making content comprehensible for English learners: The SIOP® Model.* (3rd ed.) Boston, MA: Pearson Allyn and Bacon, pp. 222–227.

How could the use of one or more features have been improved in the lesson?

Lesson Delivery:
Video Analysis and Discussion T-Chart

In your groups discuss...	On your own reflect...
How did Ms. Formoso support her language and content objectives?	What will be challenging for you in supporting your content and language objectives?
How did she promote student engagement?	What will be challenging for you in promoting student engagement?
Was the pacing of her lesson appropriate to her students' ability levels? Explain.	What will be challenging for you in determining the pacing of your lessons?

Lesson Delivery: Session Reflection

What questions do you have about this session?

What key ideas, learnings, and insights from this session will be most useful in helping your English learners comprehend the content you present to them?

Explain why.

Please answer the prompts in the Lesson Delivery section of the SIOP Model Self-Assessment on page 150 of this workbook.

Review and Assessment

10

11

12

Review and Assessment Features

27. Comprehensive **review of key vocabulary**

28. Comprehensive **review of key content concepts**

29. Regular **feedback** provided to students on their output

30. **Assessment of student comprehension and learning** of all lesson objectives throughout the lesson

Classroom Connections: Simultaneous Roundtable

Could you use the simultaneous roundtable in your classroom? If so, how?

How does it support language development for all learners?

10

11

12

Review and Assessment: Session Reflection

What questions do you have about this session?

What key ideas, learnings, and insights from this session will be most useful in helping your English learners comprehend the content you present to them?

Explain why.

Please answer the prompts in the Review and Assessment section of the SIOP Model Self-Assessment on page 150 of this workbook.

Review and Assessment: Wrap-Up

In groups, complete the following concept definition map in order to summarize key learnings about the SIOP Model.

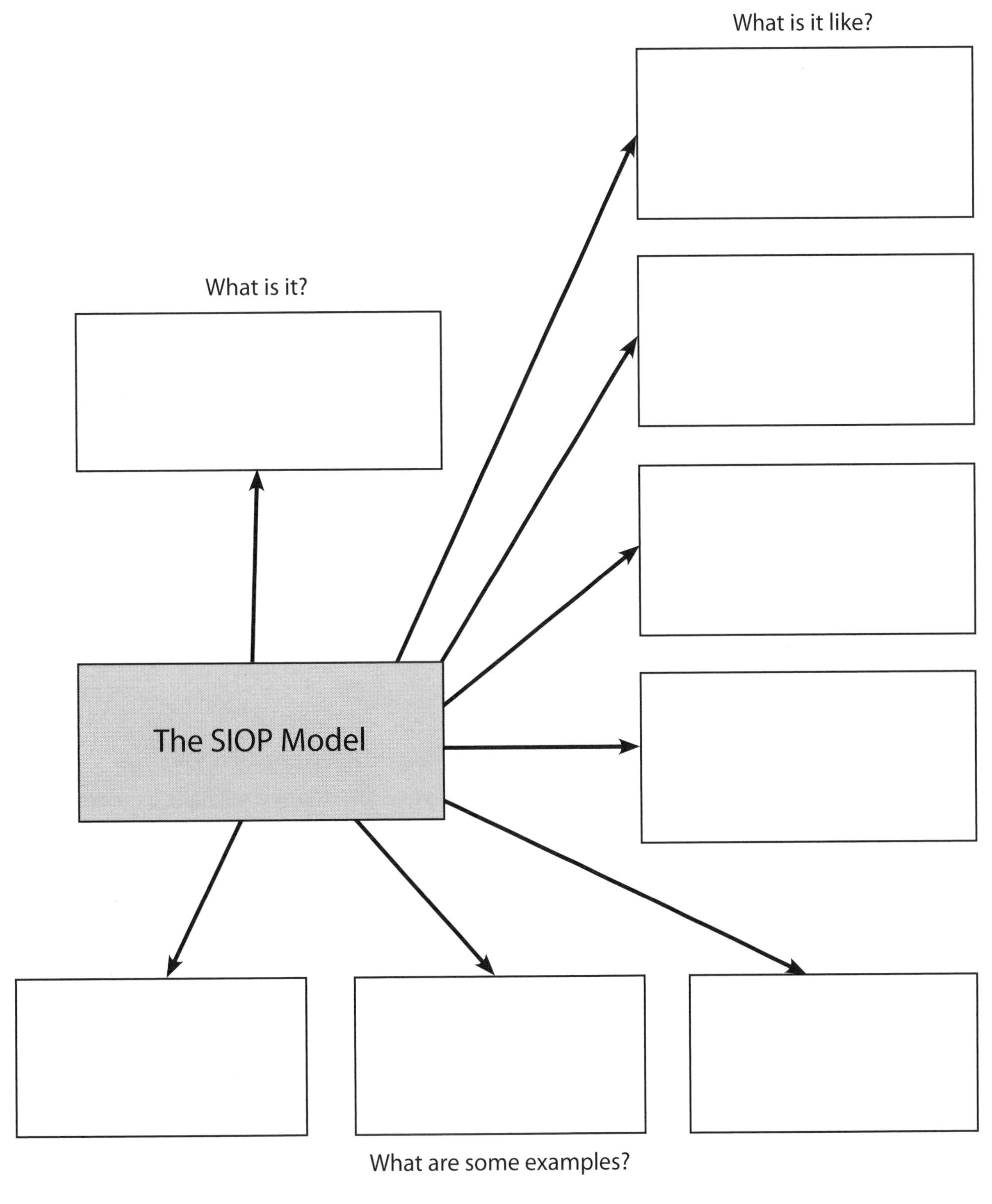

Implementing the SIOP Model

11

12

SIOP Model Implementation Action Plan: Part 1

The component I plan to focus on as I begin to implement the SIOP Model is:

____

____

The rationale behind choosing this component to focus on first is:

____

____

Action Steps	Resources Needed	Timeline During Next 2 Months

SIOP Model Implementation Action Plan: Part 1 (continued)

1. Identify at least one question or challenge you have or anticipate in implementing this component.

2. List some possible solutions or ways to address the challenge.

SIOP Model Implementation Action Plan: Part 2

Describe at least three things your group will do to support each other in implementing the SIOP components in your classrooms. Identify who will do what, and when.

What? (Actions)	Who Is Responsible?	When?

1. Think about what resources and support you will need from your administrator and list them here.

   ____

   ____

   ____

2. What are at least two steps you can take to get these resources and support from your administrator?

   ____

   ____

   ____

Implementing the SIOP Model: Session Reflection

What questions do you have about this session?

What key ideas, learnings, or insights from this session will be most useful in helping you implement the SIOP Model in your classroom and/or school?

11

12

Lesson Planning

Pre-Lesson Plan Thinking

SIOP features you are focusing on for this lesson:

____

____

Grade/Class/Subject:

Lesson Topic: ______________________________

Objectives:

Content: ______________________________

____

Language: ______________________________

____

Key Vocabulary:

____

____

Materials: (includes supplementary/adapted materials)

____

____

List adaptations you will make to the lesson that incorporate the features you are focusing on for this lesson:

Adaptation	Anticipated Effect on EL Comprehension

Pre-Lesson Plan Thinking (continued)

Use this page to create an outline of your lesson.

SIOP Features Checklist

Lesson Preparation

- ☐ **Content objectives** clearly defined, displayed, and reviewed with students
- ☐ **Language objectives** clearly defined, displayed, and reviewed with students
- ☐ **Content concepts** appropriate for age and educational background level of students
- ☐ **Supplementary materials** used to a high degree, making the lesson clear and meaningful
- ☐ **Adaptation of content** to all levels of student proficiency
- ☐ **Meaningful activities** that integrate lesson concepts with language practice opportunities for reading, writing, listening, and/or speaking

Building Background

- ☐ **Concepts explicitly linked** to students' background experiences
- ☐ **Links explicitly made** between past learning and new concepts
- ☐ **Key vocabulary** emphasized

Comprehensible Input

- ☐ **Speech** appropriate for students' proficiency levels
- ☐ **Clear explanation** of academic tasks
- ☐ **A variety of techniques** used to make content concepts clear

Strategies

- ☐ Ample opportunities provided for students to use **learning strategies**
- ☐ **Scaffolding techniques** consistently used, assisting and supporting student understanding
- ☐ A variety of **questions or tasks that promote higher-order thinking skills**

Interaction

- ☐ Frequent opportunities for **interaction** and discussion between teacher/student and among students, which encourage elaborated responses about lesson concepts
- ☐ **Grouping configurations** support language and content objectives of the lesson
- ☐ Sufficient **wait time for student responses** consistently provided
- ☐ Ample opportunities for students to **clarify key concepts in L1** as needed with aide, peer, or L1 text

SIOP Features Checklist (continued)

Practice and Application

- ☐ **Hands-on materials and/or manipulatives** provided for students to practice using new content knowledge
- ☐ Activities provided for students to **apply content and language knowledge** in the classroom
- ☐ Activities integrate all **language skills** (i.e., reading, writing, listening, and speaking)

Lesson Delivery

- ☐ **Content objectives** clearly supported by lesson delivery
- ☐ **Language objectives** clearly supported by lesson delivery
- ☐ **Students engaged** approximately 90% to 100% of the period
- ☐ **Pacing** of the lesson appropriate to students' ability levels

Review and Assessment

- ☐ Comprehensive **review of key vocabulary**
- ☐ Comprehensive **review of key content concepts**
- ☐ Regular **feedback** provided to students on their output
- ☐ **Assessment of student comprehension and learning** of all lesson objectives throughout the lesson

SIOP® Lesson Plan Template 1

Date: ____________________ Grade/Class/Subject: ____________________

Unit/Theme: ____________________ Standards: ____________________

Content Objective(s): ____________________

____

Language Objective(s): ____________________

____

Key Vocabulary	Supplementary Materials

SIOP FEATURES

Preparation	Scaffolding	Group Options
___ Adaptation of content	___ Modeling	___ Whole class
___ Links to background	___ Guided practice	___ Small groups
___ Links to past learning	___ Independent practice	___ Partners
___ Strategies incorporated	___ Comprehensible input	___ Independent
Integration of Processes	**Application**	**Assessment**
___ Reading	___ Hands-on	___ Individual
___ Writing	___ Meaningful	___ Group
___ Speaking	___ Linked to objectives	___ Written
___ Listening	___ Promotes engagement	___ Oral

Lesson Sequence:

Reflections:

SIOP® Lesson Plan Template 2

STANDARDS:

THEME:

LESSON TOPIC:

OBJECTIVES:

Language

Content

LEARNING STRATEGIES:

KEY VOCABULARY:

MATERIALS:

- -

MOTIVATION:
(Building background)

PRESENTATION:
(Language and content objectives, comprehensible input, strategies, interaction, feedback)

PRACTICE AND APPLICATION:
(Meaningful activities, interaction, strategies, practice and application, feedback)

REVIEW AND ASSESSMENT:
(Review objectives and vocabulary, assess learning)

EXTENSION:

Lesson Implementation Reflection

After you've taught the lesson you planned with your colleagues, use this page to note your reflections as part of the "plan-teach-analyze-revise" teaching cycle.

Lesson Title: ________________________ Date: ________

List the key modifications that you planned **and** implemented in your lesson to address each feature. Note the effect of the modifications that you implemented on your English learners' content comprehension.

What did you try?	What happened?

Based on your reflection, what are some changes you would make in the lesson to help English learners meet the lesson objectives?

____

____

____

____

____

____

____

Lesson Planning: Session Reflection

What questions do you have about this session?

What key ideas, learnings, or insights from this session will be most useful in helping you implement the SIOP Model in your classroom and/or school?

Appendix

SIOP Model Self-Assessment

Using the features below, mark the box that most closely represents your current teaching practices:

D = Daily O = Occasionally N = Never

	D	O	N
Lesson Preparation			
1. **Content objectives** clearly defined, displayed, and reviewed with students			
2. **Language objectives** clearly defined, displayed, and reviewed with students			
3. **Content concepts** appropriate for age and educational background level of students			
4. **Supplementary materials** used to a high degree, making the lesson clear and meaningful			
5. **Adaptation of content** (e.g., text, assignment) to all levels of student proficiency			
6. **Meaningful activities** that integrate lesson concepts (e.g., interviews, letter writing, simulations, models) with language practice opportunities for reading, writing, listening, and/or speaking			
Building Background			
7. **Concepts explicitly linked** to students' background experiences			
8. **Links explicitly made** between past learning and new concepts			
9. **Key vocabulary** emphasized (e.g., introduced, written, repeated, and highlighted for students to see)			
Comprehensible Input			
10. **Speech** appropriate for students' proficiency levels (e.g., slower rate, enunciation, and simple sentence structure for beginners)			
11. **Clear explanation** of academic tasks			
12. **A variety of techniques** used to make content concepts clear (e.g., modeling, visuals, hands-on activities, demonstrations, gestures, body language)			
Strategies			
13. Ample opportunities provided for students to use **learning strategies**			
14. **Scaffolding techniques** consistently used, assisting and supporting student understanding (e.g., think-alouds)			
15. A variety of **questions or tasks that promote higher-order thinking skills** (e.g., literal, analytical, and interpretive questions)			
Interaction			
16. Frequent opportunities for **interaction** and discussion between teacher/student and among students, which encourage elaborated responses about lesson concepts			
17. **Grouping configurations** support language and content objectives of the lesson			
18. Sufficient **wait time for student responses** consistently provided			
19. Ample opportunities for students to **clarify key concepts in L1** as needed with aide, peer, or L1 text			

Using the features below, mark the box that most closely represents your current teaching practices:

D = Daily O = Occasionally N = Never

	D	O	N
Practice and Application			
20. **Hands-on materials and/or manipulatives** provided for students to practice using new content knowledge			
21. Activities provided for students to **apply content and language knowledge** in the classroom			
22. Activities integrate all **language skills** (i.e., reading, writing, listening, and speaking)			
Lesson Delivery			
23. **Content objectives** clearly supported by lesson delivery			
24. **Language objectives** clearly supported by lesson delivery			
25. **Students engaged** approximately 90% to 100% of the period			
26. **Pacing** of the lesson appropriate to students' ability levels			
Review and Assessment			
27. Comprehensive **review of key vocabulary**			
28. Comprehensive **review of key content concepts**			
29. Regular **feedback** provided to students on their output (e.g., language, content, work)			
30. **Assessment of student comprehension and learning** of all lesson objectives (e.g., spot-checking, group response) throughout the lesson			

References

Cummins, J. (1981). The role of primary language development in promoting educational success for language minority students. In *Schooling and language minority students: A theoretical framework* (pp. 3–49). Los Angeles: Evaluation, Dissemination, and Assessment Center, California State University, Los Angeles.

Echevarria, J. and Graves, A. (2007). *Sheltered content instruction: Teaching English language learners with diverse abilities.* 3rd ed. Boston, MA: Pearson Allyn and Bacon.

Echevarria, J., Vogt, M.E., and Short, D. (2008). *Making content comprehensible for English learners: The SIOP Model.* 3rd ed. Boston, MA: Pearson Allyn and Bacon.

Glickling, E. and Thompson, V. (1992, April). *Curriculum based assessment.*

Kagan, S. (1997). *Cooperative learning.* Kagan Cooperative Learning.

Short, D., Hudec, J., and Echevarria, J. (2002). *Using the SIOP Model: Professional development manual for sheltered instruction.* Washington, DC: Center for Applied Linguistics.

Walqui, A. (2000). *Contextual factors in second language acquisition.* ERIC Digest. ERIC Document Reproduction Service No. EDO-FL-00-05.